Nic at Night

A Musical play for Kids about Nicodemus

By
KATHIE HILL

COMPANION PRODUCTS:

Listening Cassette 3280-21

Accompaniment Cassette 3280-22
SIDE A: Split-track (Voices right: Instruments left)
SIDE B: Stereo (Instruments only)

Accompaniment CD 3280-23
Split-track and Stereo Tracks

Dovetailor 3080-10

Poster Pack 3080-11

Video (Instructional) 3400-07
Providing suggestions for movement,
costuming and staging

Code 3180-08

Setting
A theater production of a biblical play, "Nic at Night"

CHARACTERS

Aunt Ellen – played by a young woman

Tyler, her nephew – a boy, age 8-12

McKenzie, her niece – a girl, age 7-8

Stage Audience – 7 to 8 other children or adults wearing dressy clothes

Chorus – Children on risers, wearing black shirts with white or metallic stars to represent the night sky

Hostess*– older girl, poised and well-groomed, wearing a formal gown

Nebbie, Becca and Sara*– children of Jesus' followers, wearing biblical era costumes

Nicodemus – Male actor made to look like an old man, in Pharisee robes (refer to costume suggestions, page 83)

Jesus (non-speaking) – young male with a kind face, in biblical costumes

Phil Pharisee, Phrank Pharisee, Phred Pharisee, Phorest Pharisee – all wearing Pharisee robes or headdresses and prayer shawls (these parts may be played by boys or girls)

Roman Guard*– boy, possibly a teenager, in guard togs

Joseph of Arimathea – male actor made to look like an old man, in Pharisee robes

* with minor dialogue changes, you may expand the number of speaking parts by dividing these and the Pharisee roles among several children.

OPTIONAL CHARACTERS

Act I suggests having 4 to 6 adults dressed in biblical costume attending to Jesus during the opening dialogue. In Act III, these same characters can enter during "The First Lord's Day" to celebrate the resurrection and sing the optional adult parts on "Christ the Lord Is Risen Today." If preschoolers are a part of the stage audience (refer to production suggestions in the DOVETAILOR), additional adults may also be seated in that area to supervise.

Solos – The thirteen children's solos and two adult solos on the recording can be expanded to eighteen children's solos.

Sequence

4

(Lights down on the risers and stage area and up on the stage audience. Choir members and stage audience enter as the *Sound Effect of an orchestra tuning is played. The choir enters from stage right and stage left. The stage audience, including Aunt Ellen, Tyler, and McKenzie, enters from down stage center [through the actual audience]. The main characters enter last and stand at the front row. The Hostess is standing in front of the on-stage seats passing out programs to the stage audience as they take their seats. The stage audience may sit or remain standing in quiet conversation, but the choir should take their places on the risers silently, and immediately turn their backs to the audience.)

HOSTESS: *(handing Aunt Ellen three programs)* Your programs.

AUNT ELLEN: *(taking them)* Thank you. Tyler … McKenzie. This is the hostess for tonight's play. She'll be introducing each act.

HOSTESS: So you've already seen it?

AUNT ELLEN: Just last week. Tonight I brought my niece and nephew.

McKENZIE: *(looking around excitedly)* Listen to the orchestra!

TYLER: *(equally enthusiastic)* Yeah. We've never been to a musical before.

HOSTESS: Well, then your aunt is very nice to bring you. Enjoy the show!

(Hostess moves among the other members of the stage audience, eventually making her way to her stage right position.)

TYLER: *(tugging at Aunt Ellen's sleeve)* What's the musical about, Aunt Ellen?

AUNT ELLEN: It's a mystery, Tyler.

McKENZIE: A mystery? What's a mystery?

TYLER: Get with it, McKenzie. A mystery is something that can't be explained. Haven't you seen those "whodunits" on TV where they get you all confused, then unravel the mystery at the end?

(Sound effect of orchestra fades out quickly. Other audience members take their seats.)

McKENZIE: *(loudly)* Hey, why did it get so quiet?

AUNT ELLEN: *(whispering)* Shhh! The play's about to begin.

*The Sound Effect of an orchestra tuning appears on the Accompaniment CD at

TYLER: *(also whispering)* But, what's it called?

AUNT ELLEN: *(even softer)* "Nic at Night!"

(Aunt Ellen, Tyler, and McKenzie take their seats. Lights down on the stage audience and up on the choir center stage as they turn to face the audience. [If backdrop with twinkle lights is used, turn on twinkle lights at this time.])

Nic at Night

Words and Music by
KATHIE HILL
Arranged by Chris Marion and John M. DeVries

CD Index Points: Top number (2-47) refers to SPLIT-TRACK. Bottom number (48-93) refers to STEREO TRACKS.

(Lights up on Hostess as she moves to her stage right spot. During Hostess's monologue, all Bible characters cross from stage left in the dark. Jesus and optional adult men and women take their places stage right at the fire. Sara, Becca, and Nebbie remain center stage while Nicodemus enters last and remains partially hidden left of the stage left tree.)

*HOSTESS: Good evening and welcome to *Nic at Night*.
Your hostess, I'll gladly be
for this play about Nicodemus, from John, Chapter 3.
Our story unfolds in three separate acts,
each one beginning at night.
In Act One we find our Lord Jesus
resting beneath stars so bright.
His followers are near to attend to His needs,
including some children we'll meet.
When who should appear—is it friend or foe?
It's Nicodemus, the chief Pharisee.

(Hostess returns to her stage right position.)

ACT I

(*Cricket sound effect starts. Jesus is facing stage right with his back to Sara, Becca, and Nebbie. He can be warming himself by the fire or be silently minstered to by the optional adults, i.e., bringing him bread or water. Sara, Becca, and Nebbie are playing with a ball and talking quietly as Nicodemus moves, rustling the tree. He appears hesitant about his next move, surveying the surroundings and situation.)

BECCA: *(pointing stage left)* Nebbie … who's that old man over there?

NEBBIE: *(not even looking)* Come on, Becca. It's too dark to see anything.

SARA: *(looking stage left)* Wait a minute! That's Nicodemus!

NEBBIE: Are you sure, Sara? Nicodemus?

SARA: *(impressed)* The superstar of the Sanhedrin!

BECCA: The biggest cog in the synagogue!!

NEBBIE: The brightest light on the Pharisee Wheel!!!

(They laugh at their own jokes.)

NEBBIE: *(confused)* But, why would Nicodemus be coming here to see Jesus … and so late at night?

BECCA: Yeah, Nebbie. The Pharisees don't believe Jesus is the Son of God. In fact, they're always complaining that He's broken one of *their* laws.

NEBBIE: Which one … number 1 or number 651?**

BECCA: *(exasperated)* Yeah. "Thou shalt not swat a fly" … or "thou shalt not swallow a gnat?"

(They groan at the thought of these silly man-made rules.)

SARA: Now, Becca. Remember, Jesus said the true law was given by God, not to make us *look* holy, but to make us look to *God* for our holiness.

NEBBIE: It's God's grace, not our goodness! Can't the Pharisees see that?

SARA: *(resolutely)* What you see depends on whose eyes you're looking through!

*The Sound Effect of crickets appears on the Accompaniment CD at
**There were exactly 651 Pharasaic laws.

What the Pharisees Saw

Words and Music by
KATHIE HILL
Arranged by Chris Marion and John M. DeVries

(Nicodemus moves past tree, toward center stage. Optional Bible adults exit stage right, leaving Jesus alone by the fire.)

BECCA: *(shocked)* Look, Nebbie. Nicodemus is coming this way.

NEBBIE: The Sanhedrin would have a camel!

(They laugh.)

SARA: No wonder he's come at night.

BECCA: Maybe he's looking for the truth?

NEBBIE: Well, he'll get that *(right hand over his heart, as if taking an oath)* and nothing but the truth!

(They laugh. As Nicodemus approaches, they become sincerely polite, out of respect to his position.)

NIC: Excuse me, children. But I am looking for a very important man. They call Him "Rabbi" or "Teacher."

SARA: That would be Jesus, sir. *(pointing stage right)* Resting over by the fire.

NIC: *(confused)* That common-looking man? *(pauses)* No, I don't think you understand. This man is called "the Messiah."

NEBBIE: *(proudly)* Yes, sir. That would be Jesus.

NIC: No, no. This is a very special person known as the "Master" ... the "Healer."

BECCA: That would be my Jesus, sir.

NIC: I'm afraid I'm confused. You see, I'm a very important person. The teacher of teachers ... the father of several sons ... the master of many servants. Yet, your answer to my question lies in this ... *(pointing to Jesus)* ordinary man?

NEBBIE: With all respect, sir, Jesus is no ordinary man.

BECCA: But, he's the answer to *every* question!

That Would Be My Jesus

Words and Music by
KATHIE HILL
Arranged by Chris Marion

Bright swing (♩ = 132)

1. Who's the teach-er's Teach - er? Who's the fa - ther's Dad?
2. Who's the mas-ter's Mas - ter? Who's the King of kings?

SOLO 2

Who's a Shep-herd to the shep-herd when's he's lost a lamb?
Who's the Lead - er to the lead - er when they're lead - er - ing?

Distributed by GENEVOX (a div. of GMG), Nashville, TN 37234.

(Nicodemus stares curiously at Jesus.)

SARA: Nicodemus? May we introduce you to Jesus?

NIC: *(chuckling)* I think you've already done that! If you'll excuse me, I'll go and introduce myself.

(Nicodemus moves stage right, crossing behind the centerstage bush. Jesus rises and takes his hand. They sit together by the fire talking softly. [Because they are not miked, their conversation should be unintelligible to the audience, but they may loosely follow the conversation contained in John 3:1-22.])

NEBBIE: Look at them, Sara! It's as if Jesus had been waiting for Nicodemus all along!

SARA: Sure seems that way. Let's listen and see what this "Nic at night" wants.

(Children move right single file to the centerstage bush. Sara is closest to the bush with Nebbie behind her and Sara behind him, each leaning over the other.)

NEBBIE: *(half-voice)* What's Nicodemus saying?

BECCA: *(whispers)* Yeah … what's Nicodemus saying?

SARA: He said he knows Jesus came from God or He couldn't have done all those miracles.

BECCA: *(proudly)* He's got that right. Jesus has healed the sick, raised the dead, and fed the multitudes!

NEBBIE: *(curiously)* What's Jesus saying?

BECCA: *(whispers)* Yeah … what's Jesus saying?

SARA: He says, *(slowly)* "No one will see the kingdom of God unless they're born again."

NEBBIE: *(confused)* But, can Nicodemus understand being "born again?"

BECCA: Yeah, Nebbie. He might believe a miracle he can *see*, but a miracle he *can't* see?

NEBBIE: *(feeling sorry for him)* Nicodemus has got to be clueless! So what's Jesus saying now?

BECCA: *(whispers)* Yeah. What's Jesus saying now?

SARA: He's telling the "snake story."

BECCA: *(not understanding)* The "snake story?"

NEBBIE: You know, from the book of Numbers* … when the children of Israel were dying of snakebite in the desert.

SARA: As a teacher, Nicodemus would know all about that!

NEBBIE: *(to Becca)* Remember, Moses lifted a snake upon a rod, saying that everyone who looked up at it and had faith in God would be saved?

SARA: Now Jesus is saying that someday He will be lifted up, and everyone who believes on Him will have eternal life!

NEBBIE: So, what's Nicodemus saying about that?

BECCA: *(whispers)* Yeah, what's Nico …

SARA: *(irritated)* Becca!

BECCA: Sorry. *(she pauses)* But, what *is* he saying?

SARA: Nicodemus doesn't understand how an old man like him could be born again.

NEBBIE: Of course, he doesn't, Sara! It's a mystery when Jesus puts a new spirit into our old body. It's like the wind … you can't see it, but you sure can feel it!

BECCA: So is Jesus telling Nicodemus what He told us?

SARA: *(happily)* Yes. And isn't it wonderful that God's love can speak to every heart?

*Numbers 21:6-9

John 3:16

Words and Music by
KATHIE HILL
Arranged by Chris Marion

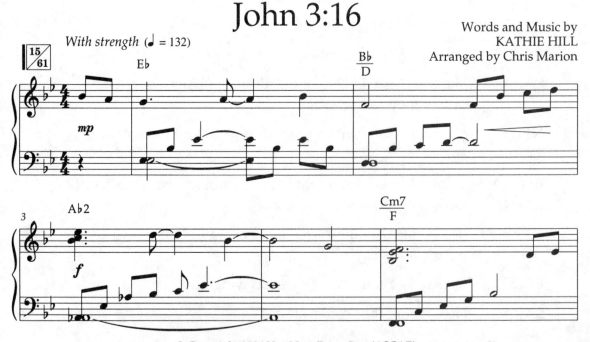

*90 years

ev - er - last - ing life.

John three six - teen means you can be born a -

gain.

*Narration on next page begins.

*BECCA: For God did not send His Son into the world to condemn the world, but to save the world through Him. Whoever believes in Him is not condemned, but whoever does not believe stands condemned already because he has not believed in the name of God's one and only Son. *(John 3:17 & 18, NIV)*

**NEBBIE: This is the verdict: Light has come into the world, but men loved darkness instead of the light because their deeds were evil. Everyone who does evil hates the light, and will not come into the light for fear that his deeds will be exposed. *(John 3:19 & 29, NIV)*

*Optionally spoken by children from choir or by Jesus.

*SARA: But whoever lives by the truth comes into the light, so that it may be seen plainly that what he has done has been done through God. *(John 3:21, NIV)*

you can be born _ a - gain

John three _ six - teen means you can be born _____ a -

gain.

(*Lights out on Bible characters centerstage as Hostess moves to stage right spot. Bible characters move quietly off stage left, taking props [fire, bush, and tree] with them.*)

HOSTESS: Will Nicodemus reach out in faith
or return to his comfort zone?
To his status among the ruling class,
to his riches and magnificent home?
We'll find out after this intermission.
Stand and stretch if you choose.
Just don't wander off too very far
or you might miss a bit of Act II.

(*Lights up on Choir.*)

Nic at Night Theme

Words and Music by
KATHIE HILL
Arranged by Chris Marion and John M. DeVries

(Stage audience applauds. Lights out on Hostess and Choir and up on stage audience. Hostess returns to stage right position. Aunt Ellen, Tyler, and McKenzie stand to speak while others may move offstage, look at programs, or talk softly.)

McKENZIE: *(whispering)* Can we talk now?

AUNT ELLEN: Yes, McKenzie. We can talk. This is the intermission.

TYLER: So, what happened, Aunt Ellen? Did Nicodemus believe in Jesus? Was he … "born again?"

AUNT ELLEN: Well, Tyler. What does it mean to be born again?

TYLER: *(pausing, embarrassed)* Uhh … I don't think I can explain it.

McKENZIE: *(remembering proudly)* Well, if you can't explain it … that makes it a *mystery!*

AUNT ELLEN: *(chuckling)* Yes, it certainly is a mystery when someone becomes a brand new person.

TYLER: You mean, like in those witness protection programs where the guy on T.V. has plastic surgery and gets a new name and they move him to a new … ?

AUNT ELLEN: *(interrupting)* No, Tyler. Those are just changes on the outside. The new birth is a change from the inside out … becoming, not an improved version of the old you, but a brand new creation!

McKENZIE: I'm sorry, Aunt Ellen, but now *I'm* clueless!

AUNT ELLEN: *(thinking)* Well, let's see, how can I illustrate this? I know. *(pinching the fold of her program to form a crude butterfly)* If I pinch my program together in the middle, it kinda looks like a what, McKenzie?

McKENZIE: A butterfly!

AUNT ELLEN: Yes. And many people use a butterfly to describe being born again!

(Lights up on choir and/or stage area.)

Born Brand New
(The Caterpillar Song)

Words by
KATHIE HILL

Music by
KATHIE HILL and CHRIS MARION
Arranged by Chris Marion

46

on - ly God can do; a mir-a-cle, a mir-a-cle, a

mir-a-cle __ from the Lord.

(Lights out on Choir and stage area. Absent stage audience members return and take their seats quietly. Choir may remain facing audience.)

TYLER: *(excited)* So, Aunt Ellen, did God do that for Nicodemus?

AUNT ELLEN: Well, that's part of the mystery, Tyler. God's plan is for everyone born here on earth to also be born into His heavenly kingdom. But God doesn't *make* anyone be born again. It's your choice to accept Jesus as Savior, just as it was Nicodemus' choice.

TYLER: So whad' he choose?

(Lights up on stage right. Hostess moves to her spot and stage audience applauds her entrance.)

McKENZIE: Shh! *(whispers)* Here comes the hostess. Maybe she'll tell us.

(Lights down on stage audience. As Hostess speaks, Nicodemus, Phil, Phrank, Phred, and Phorest quickly and quietly enter from stage left and take their places centerstage.)

ACT II

(Stage audience applauds.)

HOSTESS: Time has passed as we begin Act II
but the hour is still the same.
It's nighttime as the Sanhedrin meets,
but is Nicodemus part of their game?
These rulers want to arrest Jesus,
the Pharisees were seldom fair.
But, will there be a different outcome
because our "Nic at night" is there?

(Lights out on Hostess and up on Choir. Hostess moves to stage right position.)

Nic at Night Theme

Words and Music by
KATHIE HILL
Arranged by Chris Marion
and John M. DeVries

(Nicodemus stands distanced stage right of the four Pharisees while they are clumped together, murmuring and obviously upset. They each have a large, stringed nametag labled "Phil," "Phrank," "Phred," and "Phorest." Phorest's nametag should be turned over to the blank side. Phil may hold an optional thick law book.)

PHIL: Nicodemus? Law 453 says we can't begin a meeting of the Sanhedrin until we make sure all the religious leaders are here.

(The four Pharisees straighten their prayer shawls, moving from stage right to left in the order in which they are announced.)

NIC: *(uncomfortably)* Um … of course. Phil Pharisee?

PHIL: *(clearing his throat for all to hear)* Here.

NIC: Phred Pharisee?

PHRED: *(loudly)* Yo!

NIC: Phrank Pharisee?

PHRANK: *(precisely)* Present.

NIC: And we have a new member of the Sanhedrin. *(motioning for Phorest to turn over his nametage)* *(to Phorest)* Your name?

PHOREST: *(humbly)* Phorest. *(pause)* Phorest Pharisee.

(They laugh at his errant nametag.)

PHRED: Now, to the problem at hand. This "Jesus" healed a man on the Sabbath!!

(All but Nic gasp.)

PHIL: *(tattle-taleing)* That's breaking our Law Number 12!

PHRANK: We've seen what Phred Pharisee saw … and more! That "prophet" spoke to a woman … a *Samaritan* woman!

(All but Nic gasp.)

PHIL: *(scolding)* Number 23 and 82!

PHRANK: He not only speaks to sinners, He dines with them and offers them forgiveness of sins!

(All but Nic gasp.)

PHIL: *(with same inflection)* That's breaking 118, 246, and 398!

PHRED: I saw what Phrank Pharisee saw and heard even worse.

PHIL: What did this "Galilean" say, Phred?

PHRED: "You will look for me, but you will not find me ..."
(*John 7:34*)

PHRANK: And He added, "Where I am you cannot come!"
(*John 7:34*)

PHIL: What nonsense is this, Nicodemus? "Where I am you cannot come?"

NIC: (*finally speaking*) But, is it nonsense? Maybe Jesus meant He would be going to heaven, but the hypocrites wouldn't.

PHIL: Really, Nicodemus! If anyone were headed for heaven, it would be *us*, the Pharisees.

PHRANK: Yes. *We're* better than everyone!

PHRED: Why, you can tell by just *looking* at us, we're ...

ALL FOUR: (*striking a collective pompous pose*) Practically perfect!

(*Guard marches in from stage left, stopping downstage left of the four Pharisees.*)

PHIL: Ahh ... here's our man.

GUARD: (*At attention, saluting, and looking straight ahead at all times.*) The Roman guard. As you requested, *Sir!*

PHIL: Guard, did you arrest this imposter?

GUARD: No, *Sir!* Jesus has broken no law, *Sir!* And by my account, no one ever spoke the way this man does, *Sir!*
(*John 7:46*)

PHIL: Ha! He may have tricked you, soldier. But I'm sure none of us Pharisees believe this Jesus. Right, Nicodemus? (*silence*)

PHRANK: (*looking at Nicodemus*) Nicodemus? (*silence*)

ALL FOUR: (*staring Nicodemus down*) Nic??

NIC: (*sighing*) Does our law condemn anyone without first hearing him out?

PHIL: (*shocked*) Hear him out?

PHRANK: I'd like to hear him out. Outta town!

PHOREST: (*peaceably*) You know ... my Mama always said ...

PHRED:	(*interrupting*) Come on, Phorest ... a "prophet" from "Galilee!" Now I'd call that "stupid."
PHOREST:	(*modestly*) Like my mama always said, "Stupid is as stupid does."
PHIL:	(*taking charge*) We'll have to take care of this matter ourselves. (*giving Nic a disapproving glance*) With or *without* Nicodemus.
PHRANK:	(*snippy*) Yeah. Did he become a secret disciple or something?
PHRED:	(*crossing stage left behind Phorest*) Come on, Phorest. Let's go.
PHIL:	(*pompously*) Yes. And on our way, we'll discuss our (*holding up law book*) "Pharisee Philosophy of Life."

(*Phrank and Phil cross behind Phorest.*)

PHOREST:	(*thoughfully*) You know, my mama always said, "Life is like a box of ..."
PHIL:	(*yanking Phorest off mike*) Give it up, Phorest!!

(*The four Pharisees exit stage left as Nicodemus crosses to the Guard.*)

GUARD:	Permission to ask you something, *Sir*?
NIC:	(*patting his shoulder*) At ease, soldier. What is it?
GUARD:	(*relaxing*) Well. Are you a secret disciple? A believer in Jesus? Or do you just like to annoy your friends by taking up for Him.
NIC:	No. I've spoken with Jesus.
GUARD:	(*impressed*) You have? What did you find out about Him?
NIC:	The question should be, "What did I find out about Nicodemus?"
GUARD:	And what was that, sir?
NIC:	That in spite of all my education, my position, and my good intentions, the old Nicodemus was lost in the darkness of sin.
GUARD:	So ... tell me, sir. What happened?

(*Lights up on Choir.*)

In the Dark

Words and Music by
KATHIE HILL
Arranged by Chris Marion

First time - NIC
Second time - CHOIR

I was too — a - shamed — to meet Him in — the day. — —
dark is like — the night, — a life with-out — the Lord; — a

So when eve - ning came, — — I slipped a - way. — But be -
heart that's filled — with sin — that God can't ig - nore. — But when

GUARD: Your secret's safe with me, Nicodemus.

NIC: *(touching Guard's shoulder)* I just pray it will become your
           secret, too.

GUARD: *(saluting)* Yes, *Sir!*

*(Lights out on centerstage. Nicodemus and guard exit stage left. Lights up
on stage right as Hostess takes her spot.)*

HOSTESS: A secret disciple? In a moment we'll see
           If Nic keeps his secret as we move to Act III.

(Hostess returns to stage right position. Lights up on Choir.)

Nic at Night Theme

Words and Music by
KATHIE HILL
Arranged by Chris Marion and John M. DeVries

(Stage audience applauds. Lights out on Choir and up on stage audience at stage left. Aunt Ellen, Tyler, and McKenzie stand as other stage audience members move or converse softly.)

McKENZIE: Wow, Aunt Ellen, I've heard of a secret agent, but never a secret disciple.

TYLER: But, how could Nicodemus be a Christian if he didn't want everyone to know?

AUNT ELLEN: That's a good question.

McKENZIE: Are you a Christian, Tyler?

TYLER: You know I am!

McKENZIE: Yeah, but you never invite your friends to church and when the pastor asked you to read the scripture on Children's Sunday, you pretended to have laryngitis!

TYLER: *(his voice suddenly hoarse)* So, what if? *(clearing his throat)* So, what if I did?

McKENZIE: So. Nicodemus was a secret disciple … and Tyler, too!

Secret Disciples

Words and Music by
KATHIE HILL
Arranged by Chris Marion

*"Stand Up, Stand Up for Jesus," Words by GEORGE DUFFIELD, JR.; Music by GEORGE J. WEBB.

(Lights out on choir)

AUNT ELLEN: Tyler, there are occasions when all of us are tempted to be secret disciples. Like Nicodemus, we might even have to keep our faith a secret for a while. But when the time came for him to stand up for Jesus, Nicodemus was willing to …

(Lights up on stage right as Hostess takes her spot.)

McKENZIE: Shhh! Don't spoil the mystery, Aunt Ellen.

TYLER: Yeah … here comes the hostess with Act III.

(Stage audience applauds. Lights out on stage left. Sara, Nebbie, and Becca enter stage left and quietly take their places centerstage.)

ACT III

HOSTESS: Welcome back to our play in three acts,
the third of which starts rather sadly.
The Pharisees arrested Jesus.
He was mocked and beaten badly.
And though our Savior had done nothing wrong
they plotted and put Him to death.
And now Sara, Nebbie, and Becca are alone,
With nothing but His promises left.

(Lights down on stage right as Hostess returns to her position. Lights up centerstage and on Choir. Sara, Nebbie, and Becca are comforting each other as Becca is crying into handkerchief.)

The First Lord's Day Medley

Arranged by Chris Marion

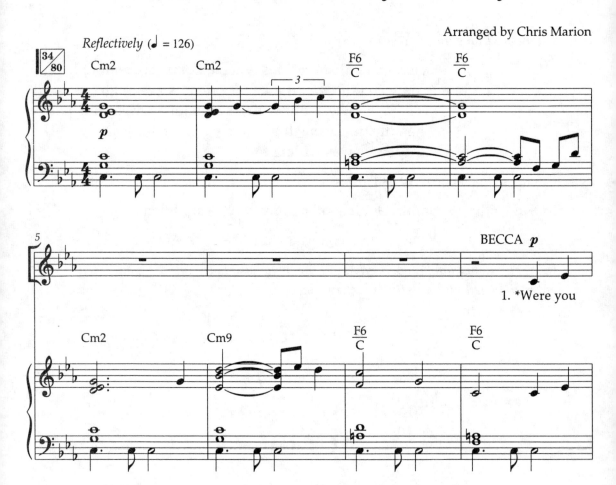

(1) SARA: Don't cry, Becca.
(2) NEBBIE: Don't you remember the snake story?
(3) NIC: I brought ointments for his body.

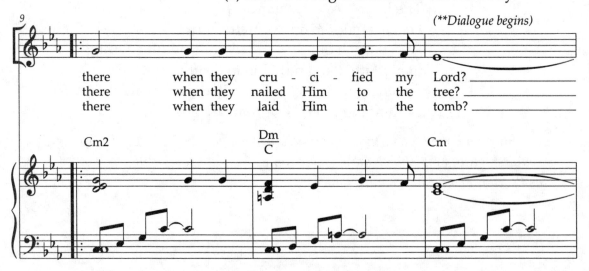

*"Were You There," Words Negro Spiritual; Music adapted by John W. Work, Jr. and Frederick J. Work.

Arrangement © copyright 1996 Van Ness Press, Inc. (ASCAP).
Distributed by GENEVOX (a div. of GMG), Nashville, TN 37234.

Were you there when they cru - ci - fied my Lord?
Were you there when they nailed Him to the tree?
Were you there when they laid Him in the tomb?

*(1) NEBBIE: Think of His promises.
(2) NEBBIE: How He'd be lifted up to save others.
(3) NIC: My friend, Joseph, provided that tomb.

(*Dialogue begins.)

Oh, _____ some - times it caus - es me to trem - ble,

trem - ble,   trem - ble.   Were   you

there   when they   cru - ci - fied   my   Lord?
there   when they   nailed   Him   to   the   tree?
there   when they   laid   Him   in   the

*(1) SARA: Jesus said He was going to die, but He also said
He'd be raised again! *(Matt. 27:63)*

(2) *(Nicodemus enters quietly from stage right.)*

     NIC: I know just how you feel, children.

     SARA & NEBBIE: Oh, Nicodemus!

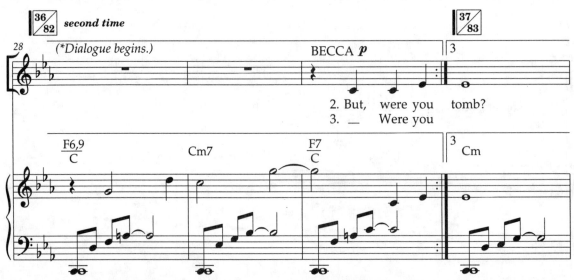

(*Dialogue begins.*)   BECCA *p*

2. But, were you   tomb?
3. __ Were you

*NIC: He died between two criminals. But, we buried Him like a king.

BECCA: *(heart-felt)* King Jesus.

*Dialogue begins.

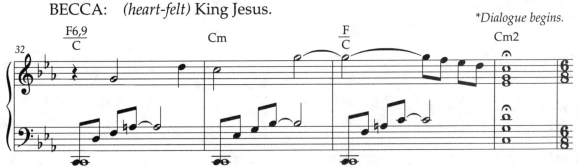

**SARA: The bells! Listen. What do they mean?

(Joseph of Arimathea comes running from stage right with optional grave linens. Flood lights behind risers light upstage area, backdrop twinkle lights disappear.)

NIC: Look! It's my friend, Joseph of Arimathea! He's coming from the tomb!

JOSEPH: *(catching his breath, excitedly)* He is risen! Nicodemus, Jesus is risen from the dead!

NEBBIE: What?

JOSEPH: *(joyously)* The Son has risen!

NIC: *(with upraised hands)* We're no longer disciples by night, Joseph. The day of the Lord has arrived.

ALL: *(hugging each other)* Hallelujah! He is risen, indeed!

***Keep track loud enough for bells to be heard.*

First time - CHOIR
Second time - SOLO

*1. They rolled the stone be-fore the door as
an - gel stood be-fore the tomb with

in the grave He lay. God raised Him up, our
won - drous words of cheer. "Weep no more for

Both times - CHOIR

liv - ing Lord, on this, the first Lord's Day. We
Him who died, for Je - sus is not here!"

sing for joy, we sing for joy, with lov - ing thanks we

*"The First Lord's Day," Words and music by WILLIAM N. McELRATH.

*Additional words and music by KATHIE HILL.

cho - sen ones! _____ The earth is dressed in green this day, to greet our ris - en Lord. We praise Him for He lives a - gain, He keeps His prom - ised Word. We sing for joy, we

*"Christ the Lord Is Risen Today," Words by CHARLES WESLEY; Music *Lyra Davidica.*

*Cue notes for adults.

(Stage audience applauds. Lights up on stage right as Hostess moves to spot.)

HOSTESS: Our play now ends on the happiest note
       Jesus waits to welcome us into His heavenly home.
       And what is the mystery
       of "Nic at night's" new birth?
       The answer is that Jesus died for everyone on earth.
       The godly and the righteous,
       like our hero Nicodemus.
       Or the criminals and hypocrites,
       the selfish and the meanest.
       And what a mystery that is!
       That the wicked and the nice,
       through grace receive a brand new birth
       when they trust in Jesus Christ.
       Undeserved, it can't be earned, yet it's easily explained
       It's God's free gift to you and me,
       by trusting on His name.

(Half light on stage left.)

TYLER: *(whispering)* So the mystery is that everyone needs to
       be born again?

McKENZIE: *(whispering)* That's why God sent His only Son!

AUNT ELLEN: *(hugging her tightly)* That's right, McKenzie!

McKENZIE: Yeah!

(Aunt Ellen hugs Tyler and McKenzie as the Hostess continues.)

HOSTESS: And as we've learned from Nicodemus,
       in this play with three parts,
       there are three things we must do
       to trust God with all our hearts.
       So, as we close, I'll share with you
       these necessary facts
       and pray, like "Nic at night,"
       your life is seen in these three acts.

(Lights up on Choir. Hostess returns to stage right position.)

Acts I, II, and III

Words and Music by
KATHIE HILL
Arranged by Chris Marion

(All stage lights up, stage audience stands and applauds.)
(Use the beginning instrumental section for bows in the following order:)
1. *Joseph of Arimathea and Guard*
2. *Phil, Phrank, Phred, and Phorest*
3. *Hostess*
4. *Nebbie, Becca, and Sara*
5. *Aunt Ellen, Tyler, and McKenzie*
6. *Jesus and Nicodemus*

Nic at Night Reprise

Words and Music by
KATHIE HILL
Arranged by Chris Marion and John M. DeVries

34

Here's the sto-ry of Nic at night, What the Sav-ior said to

Dm7　　G9　　C　　C#°7　　Dm7　　G9

37

that good man __ and what be- gan __ When Je - sus met with

C　　C7/Bb　　Dm/A　　Fm6/Ab　　C/G　　G7

40

Nic at night. Je - sus met with Nic, Nic, Nic, Nic,

G7/B　　G7　　C　　C/G　　G　　N.C.

44

(Stage audience applauds.)

Nic, Nic, Nic, Nic, Nic, Nic, Nic, Nic, Nic at night!

Gm7　　Eb2/G　　G7　　B　　C

Instrumental exit music appears on the Accompaniment CD at **47**

Set and Props

General

- Black flat backdrop – optional with miniature lights to look like a starry sky; or a backdrop painting of a night sky with moon and stars
- Risers for choir
- Chairs for stage audience
- Folded mock programs for each person in stage audience

Act I

- 6-to 8-foot ficus or artificial tree
- 3- to 4-foot artificial or real bush
- Campfire made from fake logs and yellow, red, and orange cellophane or plastic, with optional light beneath
- Clay cup, loaf of bread, things adults bring Jesus
- Ball for Nebbie, Becca, and Sara

Act II

- 12-by-5-inch stringed name tags for "Phil," "Phrank," "Phred," and "Phorest"
- Thick law book for Phil – *optional*

Act III

- Handkerchief for Sara – *optional*
- Flood lights set behind risers for resurrection scene
- Grave linens for Joseph to carry out when announcing Jesus' resurrection – *optional*

The following props and suggestions are optional. Their use is described and demonstrated on the Instructional Video (Code: 3400-07).

Act I

- "God Eyes" for "What the Pharisees Saw"
- Slides of children and adults for "John 3:16"

Act II

- Butterfly costumes for "Born Brand New"
- Hats and trenchcoats for "Secret Disciples"

Act III

- 6-to 8-foot ficus or real tree
- Silk, plastic or real flowers to form a floral cross for "Christ the Lord Is Risen Today"
- 3-by-5-foot green Styrofoam or florist foam cross, wired to back of tree
- Banners for "Acts I, II, and III"

Costumes

Nicodemus, Joseph of Arimathea, and Pharisees:

• **Robes:** Use the drawing of Nicodemus from the cover and a commercial pattern to create a floor-length, long-sleeved white tunic. (Bap-tismal robes or white choir robes will work.)

Secure the robe at the waist with a strip of black fabric (6 inches wide by 6 feet long) tied in the front. Attach tassels or bells to each end.

Make a sleeveless black tunic or floor length vest to wear over the white long-sleeved tunic. Gather the tunic or vest at the shoulder seam to create more volume.

Over the sleeveless tunic, place a 6-inch wide prayer shawl, long enough to go around the neck with ends hanging 8 to 10 inches from the floor. The shawl may be white, black, or brightly colored with embroidery, beading, tassels, or bells on the ends.

• **The headdress:** You need a 3-foot square of black or black-and-white-striped fabric and a white bandanna. Fold the white bandanna in half diagonally from corner to corner. Continue folding until you have an approximately 3-inch wide headband.

Lay the folded bandanna on the floor or a table. Place the edge of one side of the black fabric centered over the bandanna. Using three safety pins, pin the edge of the fabric to the center of the bandanna and six inches from either end of the bandanna.

Drape the headdress over the head, black fabric side in, placing the bandanna across the forehead. Tie the bandanna behind the head, either over or under the fabric, so that the black fabric drapes over the back of the head.

NOTE: Because of their position among the Pharisees, Nicodemus and Joseph of Arimathea's costumes should be the most ornate, followed by Phil, then Phrank and Phred. Phorest's costume should be the most modest. Optional: If these four are doubling as chorus members create headdress and prayer shawls only. The prayer shawl will cover the stars on the t-shirts and the remainder of their outfit will be black.

Guard: Create an authentic looking costume, using cardboard chest plates, skirts, sandals, and a helmet (available at most costume shops). Or buy or borrow a set of toy plastic "spiritual armor" (available at most Christian book stores). You may also make armor from gray or silver metallic poster board.

All other Bible Characters:

• **Jesus** should be dressed in a traditional Bible costume, such as a blue- or brown-belted tunic and sleeveless floor-length vest. Do not put Him in bright colors, since these were only worn by rich men of His day.

• **Optional adult followers** should be dressed similarly.

• **Sara, Becca,** and **Nebbie** can be in traditional Bible costumes (tunics, belts, sandals, optional headdress).

Present-day Characters

• The **hostess** should be dressed in formal attire, possibly a vintage-looking prom dress to add to the nostalgia of the "Nic at Night Theme."

• **Aunt Ellen** should wear a dressy contemporary outfit, slacks or skirt.

• **McKenzie** and **Tyler** should wear their Sunday best.

• **Stage audience members** should dress in appropriate present-day theater attire.

Choir: Whether or not you use a starry backdrop, let the children become the night sky. Each should wear black sweatpants, leggings, pants, or black jeans and black long-sleeved turtlenecks, t-shirts, or sweatshirts. Either silk screen the enclosed pattern (page 86) of stars, or adhere your own white felt or gold lame stars to their shirts with craft glue, fusible bonding, or spray mount stars cut from gold or white wrapping paper.

Lighting

Specific lighting cues are given throughout the *Nic at Night* script. If you have access to one or more spotlights, follow the lighting directions to spot the person(s) speaking. If you have no special lighting, instruct the children to give their complete attention to those characters who are talking or singing, thus drawing the audience's attention to the choir or those characters.

The flood lights placed between the choir risers and optional backdrop should be bright enough that when engaged they create the essence of daybreak. If you have miniature lights in your backdrop, disengage these lights when the flood lights are turned on. If you have a moon as a part of your backdrop, replace it with a sun as you turn on the flood lights at the beginning of the song, "The First Lord's Day."

Stage Diagram

ACT I

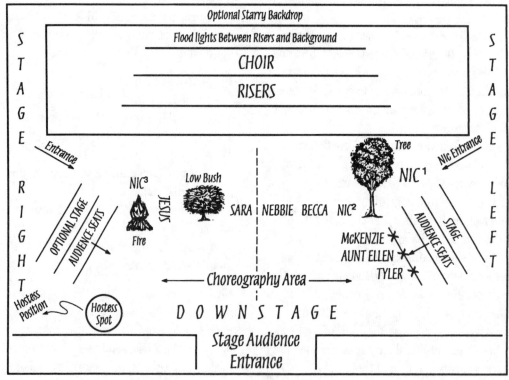

ACT II

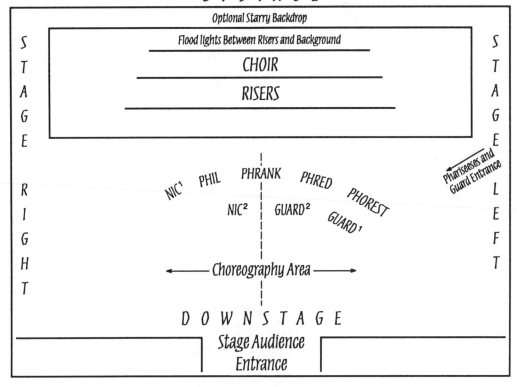

ACT III

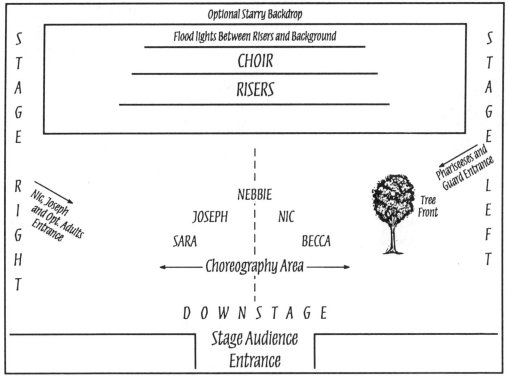

Left – CONFIGURATION OF STARS FOR BLACK SHIRTS – *Right*

Made for Praise

is designed for two age groups—YOUNGER CHILDREN, Kindergarten through Grade 3 (emphasizing grades 1–2) and OLDER CHILDREN, Grades 3–6, (emphasizing grades 4–5). Published twice a year, each volume contains approximately 20 songs and 16 weeks of teaching material.

• A **Leader's Guide** for each age level is packaged in a sturdy clamshell binder and contains over 100 pages of teaching ideas, songs, reproducible activity pages, sign language, choreography, drama, and choral readings related to the songs. Also included are two Choir Books, two rehearsal and performance cassettes *and* CDs, and a 30-minute demonstration video.

• **Choir Books** for each age group contain all songs and hymns as well as 16 color teaching pages.

• **ChoirCassettes**, take-home cassettes packaged in boxes of 10, are available for individual learning and enjoyment at home.

Order today from your music supplier!
Or call 1-800-436-3869.

Are You Challenged...
Musically? Organizationally? Creatively?

Kathie Hill brings a companion product to children's musicals that does everything except hug and applaud!

The DOVETAILOR

Through Genevox Music Group and its children's division, Dovetail Music, Kathie Hill has developed teaching, organizational and production materials that will lead even the novice director from pre-planned weekly rehearsals through a successful production.

The DOVETAILOR is designed to fully explore the educational content in each song of a Dovetail musical. Teaching Outlines specify the primary musical principles and main spiritual principles which are fleshed out in creative Teaching Activities. The activities vary from worksheets to posters, games, stories and simple crafts which are completed in large group, small group or individually.

Color-coded Teaching Cards break each song into achievable sections and lead the director measure-by-measure in covering selected musical concepts in each piece. Rehearsal Plan Sheets organize the Teaching Cards and their corresponding Teaching Activities into a minimum of 12 rehearsals. **The DOVETAILOR** also contains timesaving helps for scheduling, auditioning, and casting your production. Even a comprehensive kick-off party plan is outlined to maximize your enrollment efforts, along with promotional posters, postcards, nametags and clip art.

All this is packaged in an accessible three-ring binder with divided sections - and all forms, worksheets, cards, outlines and other aids are reproducible. In addition, each **DOVETAILOR** comes with a listening cassette, choral book and over-sized posters. Even more important, a 10% discount or rebate on the accompaniment tape for that Dovetail musical is included in each **DOVETAILOR!** AND included in the **Nic at Night** DOVETAILOR is a coupon towards the purchase of the Instructional Video (Code 3400-07).

The DOVETAILOR is available for the following Dovetail musicals:

Nic at Night (3080-10)
AmeriKids (3080-08)
Truth Works! (3080-06)
Christmas In Egypt (3080-04)
Hans Bronson's Gold Medal Mission (3080-02)
Prime Time Christmas (3080-01)
Go, Go Jonah (4150-40)
The Don't Be Afraid Brigade (4154-23)

Order today from your music supplier!
Or call 1-800-436-3869.

DOVETAIL MUSIC
127 Ninth Avenue, N.
Nashville, TN 37234